Preparatory Level

Specific Skill Series

Following Directions

Richard A. Boning

Fifth Edition

WITHDRAWN

SRA/McGraw-Hill

Columbus, Ohio

Cover, Back Cover, ZEFA/Germany/The Stock Market

SRA/McGraw-Hill

A Division of The **McGraw·Hill** Companies

Printed in the United States of America.

Send all inquiries to:
    SRA/McGraw-Hill
    8787 Orion Place
    Columbus, OH 43240-4027

ISBN 0-02-687930-1

    5 6 7 IPC 03 02 01

To the Teacher

PURPOSE:
FOLLOWING DIRECTIONS is designed to develop skill in reading, understanding, and following instructions and directions. Proficiency in this basic skill is essential for success in every school subject and in nonacademic activities as well.

FOR WHOM:
The skill of FOLLOWING DIRECTIONS is developed through a series of books spanning ten levels (Picture, Preparatory, A, B, C, D, E, F, G, H). The Picture Level is for pupils who have not acquired a basic sight vocabulary. The Preparatory Level is for pupils who have a basic sight vocabulary but are not yet ready for the first-grade-level book. Books A through H are appropriate for pupils who can read on levels one through eight, respectively. **The use of the *Specific Skill Series Placement Test* is recommended to determine the appropriate level.**

THE NEW EDITION:
The fifth edition of the *Specific Skill Series* maintains the quality and focus that has distinguished this program for more than 25 years. A key element central to the program's success has been the unique nature of the reading selections. Nonfiction pieces about current topics have been designed to stimulate the interest of students, motivating them to use the comprehension strategies they have learned to further their reading. To keep this important aspect of the program intact, a percentage of the reading selections have been replaced in order to ensure the continued relevance of the subject material.

In addition, a significant percentage of the artwork in the program has been replaced to give the books a contemporary look. The cover photographs are designed to appeal to readers of all ages.

SESSIONS:
Short practice sessions are the most effective. It is desirable to have a practice session every day or every other day, using a few units each session.

SCORING:
Pupils should record their answers on the reproducible worksheets. The worksheets make scoring easier and provide uniform records of the pupils' work. Using worksheets also avoids consuming the exercise books.

To the Teacher

It is important for pupils to know how well they are doing. For this reason, units should be scored as soon as they have been completed. Then a discussion can be held in which pupils justify their choices. (The Integrated Language Activities, many of which are open-ended, do not lend themselves to an objective score; thus there are no answer keys for these pages.)

GENERAL INFORMATION ON *FOLLOWING DIRECTIONS*:

FOLLOWING DIRECTIONS focuses attention on four types of directions. The *testing and drilling* directions are like those in most textbooks and workbooks. Mastery of this type, so vital to school success, is stressed throughout FOLLOWING DIRECTIONS. The second type of direction is found in science books and involves *experimenting*. Such material requires the reader to find an answer to a problem or provides the reader with an example of practical application of a principle.

The third type of direction, *assembling*, deals with parts or ingredients and the order and way in which they are put together. Here the purpose is to make or create, rather than to solve a problem or demonstrate a principle.

Directions which tell how to do something are *performing* directions. They accent the steps in learning to do something new. The focus is on the performance rather than on the product.

SUGGESTED STEPS:

On levels A-H, pupils read the information above the first line. Then they answer the questions *below* this line. (Pupils are *not* to respond in writing to information *above* the first line; they are only to study it. Pupils should not write or mark anything in this book.) On the Picture Level, pupils tell if a picture correctly follows the directions. On the Preparatory Level, pupils tell which picture out of two correctly follows the directions.

Additional information on using FOLLOWING DIRECTIONS with pupils will be found in the **Specific Skill Series Teacher's Manual**.

RELATED MATERIALS:

Specific Skill Series Placement Tests, which enable the teacher to place pupils at their appropriate levels in each skill, are available for the Elementary (Pre-1–6) and Midway (4–8) grade levels.

Following directions is an important part of your life. At home, your parents may say, "Put away your toys." In school, your teacher may say, "Write your name at the top of your paper." On the street, the crossing guard may say, "Do not cross yet."

Following directions is like trying to find your way with a map. If you follow the map correctly, you will get where you want to go. If you make a mistake, you will get lost.

It is important to understand directions. It is important to follow them correctly.

Think about directions carefully. Ask yourself questions like these: What do the directions tell me to do? Do I understand all the words in the directions? Should I do one thing before I do another?

In this book, you will read directions to do something. Under each direction are two pictures. In one picture, someone is following the directions correctly. In the other picture, a person is not following the directions. Ask yourself, "Who is following the directions?" Then answer the question, "Which picture is right?" Choose the picture that shows someone following the directions.

DIRECTIONS:

Eat an apple.

A   B

Which picture is right?

(A) or (B)

DIRECTIONS:

Go to sleep.

A   B

Which picture is right?

(A) or (B)

DIRECTIONS:

Make a cake.

A   B

Which picture is right?

(A) or (B)

DIRECTIONS:

Help the dog.

A   B

Which picture is right?

(A) or (B)

DIRECTIONS:

Do not walk on the grass.

A   B

Which picture is right?

(A) or (B)

DIRECTIONS:

Play with the baby.

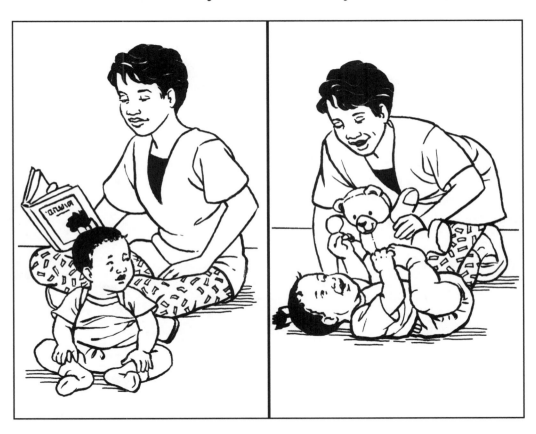

| A | B |

Which picture is right?

(A) or (B)

DIRECTIONS:

Go into the car.

A   B

Which picture is right?

(A) or (B)

DIRECTIONS:

Stay out of the rain.

A   B

Which picture is right?

(A) or (B)

DIRECTIONS:

Walk around the water.

A   B

Which picture is right?

(A) or (B)

DIRECTIONS:

Do something funny.

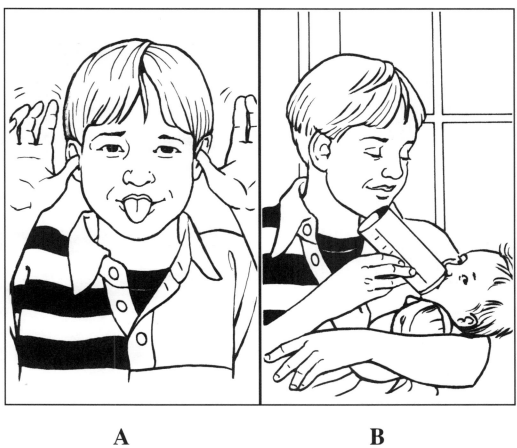

A   B

Which picture is right?

(A) or (B)

DIRECTIONS:

Ask your mother.

A   B

Which picture is right?

(A) or (B)

DIRECTIONS:

Put your toys away.

A   B

Which picture is right?

(A) or (B)

A. Exercising Your Skill

Draw a daisy. Follow the directions.

1. Start with a green stem.
2. Add 8 petals at the top. Make them white.
3. Put a yellow circle in the center.
4. Write a word under your picture. Use the word that tells about the daisy:

tree   car   flower   boat

B. Expanding Your Skill

Draw three shapes in a row like this one △.

Then do this:
1. Go back to the first shape.
2. Put your pencil in the middle of the bottom line. Draw a line down.
3. Do this for each shape.
4. Color the three shapes green.

Now you have three trees! Where might these trees be found? Write the answer under the trees.

C. Exploring Language

Read the words.

tree house grass

cup bush leaf

rose weed rock

Which words name things that grow? Write only the words that name growing things. Write each one in a color it might be.

D. Expressing Yourself

Read the questions. Write the answers.

1. Did you ever plant flower seeds?
2. Did you use a flower pot?
3. What did you put in the pot first?
4. Where did you put the flower pot?
5. Did you water the seeds?

Pick something that is easy to grow. Tell how to plant it and how to care for it.

DIRECTIONS:

Show me the book.

A   B

Which picture is right?

(A) or (B)

DIRECTIONS:

Do not jump on the bed.

A   B

Which picture is right?

(A) or (B)

DIRECTIONS:

Pet the little cat.

A   B

Which picture is right?

(A) or (B)

DIRECTIONS:

Sit in the wagon.

A   B

Which picture is right?

(A) or (B)

DIRECTIONS:

Look at the goat.

A   B

Which picture is right?

(A) or (B)

DIRECTIONS:

Run down the road.

A   B

Which picture is right?

(A) or (B)

DIRECTIONS:

Do your work now.

A B

Which picture is right?

(A) or (B)

DIRECTIONS:

Ride on the bike.

A   B

Which picture is right?

(A) or (B)

DIRECTIONS:

Get the ball.

A   B

Which picture is right?

(A) or (B)

DIRECTIONS:

Stay in the house.

A   B

Which picture is right?

(A) or (B)

DIRECTIONS:

Feed the birds.

A   B

Which picture is right?

(A) or (B)

DIRECTIONS:

Stand on your hands.

A   B

Which picture is right?

(A) or (B)

A. Exercising Your Skill

Draw a picture of a girl running. Draw a picture of a boy standing on his hands. Color your pictures. Use four or more colors.

B. Expanding Your Skill

Play "Simon Says." Pick a person to be the leader. Follow the directions only if the leader says, "Simon says . . . ."

C. Exploring Language

These words are spelled backward. Write all of them the right way. Circle the games that are played with a ball.

llabesab	ssot
hctocspoh	gat
epor pmuj	llabkcik

D. Expressing Yourself

Do one of these things.

1. Pick a game you know.
   Work with a classmate who knows how to play it.
   Talk about how to play it.
   Make up a list of directions and rules.

2. Play "Giant Steps." Think about how the leader gives the rest of the players directions. Think about how the players follow the directions.

DIRECTIONS:

Let the fish go.

A   B

Which picture is right?

(A) or (B)

DIRECTIONS:

Take two books home.

A   B

Which picture is right?

(A) or (B)

DIRECTIONS:

Ask your father.

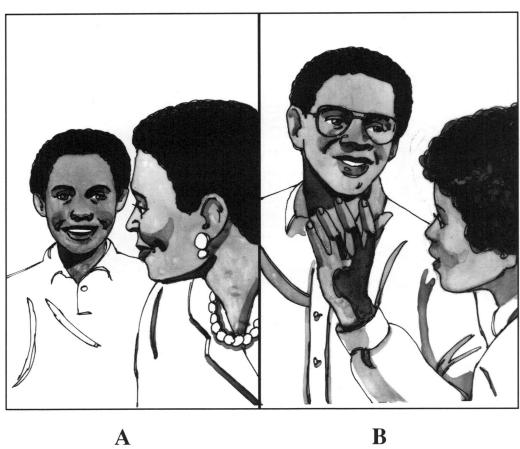

A   B

Which picture is right?

(A) or (B)

DIRECTIONS:

Do not sit in the sun.

A	**B**

Which picture is right?

(A) or (B)

DIRECTIONS:

Paint the boat.

A   B

Which picture is right?

(A) or (B)

DIRECTIONS:

Play with the ball.

A   **B**

Which picture is right?

(A) or (B)

DIRECTIONS:

Show me the cat.

A   B

Which picture is right?

(A) or (B)

DIRECTIONS:

Look at his feet.

A   B

Which picture is right?

(A) or (B)

DIRECTIONS:

Put on the hat.

A   B

Which picture is right?

(A) or (B)

DIRECTIONS:

Do not run in the house.

A   B

Which picture is right?

(A) or (B)

DIRECTIONS:

Pet the big dog.

A   B

Which picture is right?

(A) or (B)

DIRECTIONS:

Read the book to Mother.

A   B

Which picture is right?

(A) or (B)

DIRECTIONS:

Stop the pig.

A   B

Which picture is right?

(A) or (B)

DIRECTIONS:

Take the little ball.

A   B

Which picture is right?

(A) or (B)

A. Exercising Your Skill

Look at the picture. Follow the directions.

1. Write an **R** if it is a rainy day.
   Write an **S** if it is a sunny day.
2. Write a **W** if the girl is walking.
   Write an **R** if the girl is riding.
3. Write an **S** if she is going to school.
   Write an **H** if she is going home.

B. Expanding Your Skill

Tell a classmate how to get from your classroom to another room in your school. Do you go downstairs or upstairs? Do you turn a corner? Where do you go?

C. Exploring Language

Read the words. Then follow the directions.

airplane   train   bus   boat

1. Write the name of the thing that travels on tracks. Use a blue crayon.
2. Write the name of the thing that travels in the air. Use an orange crayon.
3. Write the name of the thing that travels in the water. Use a green crayon.
4. Write the name of the thing that travels on roads. Use a yellow crayon.

D. Expressing Yourself

Do one of these things.

1. Draw a picture of your favorite way to travel. Tell a classmate about how to have a fun time traveling this way.

2. Tell the class how to ski, fly a plane, drive a bus, or row a boat. Use your imagination!

DIRECTIONS:

Do not ride fast.

A   B

Which picture is right?

(A) or (B)

DIRECTIONS:

Work in the house.

A   B

Which picture is right?

(A) or (B)

DIRECTIONS:

Help Father make the boat.

A   B

Which picture is right?

(A) or (B)

DIRECTIONS:

Get your new coat.

A   B

Which picture is right?

(A) or (B)

DIRECTIONS:

Go to bed.

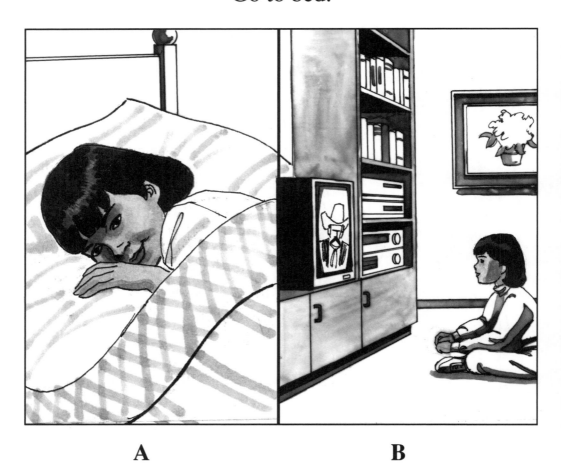

A   B

Which picture is right?

(A) or (B)

DIRECTIONS:

Eat the cake.

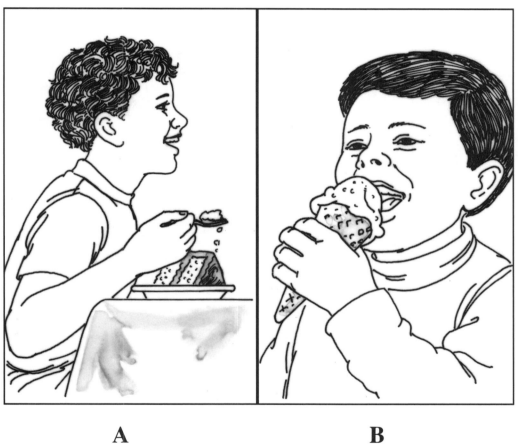

A   B

Which picture is right?

(A) or (B)

DIRECTIONS:

Put the baby to bed.

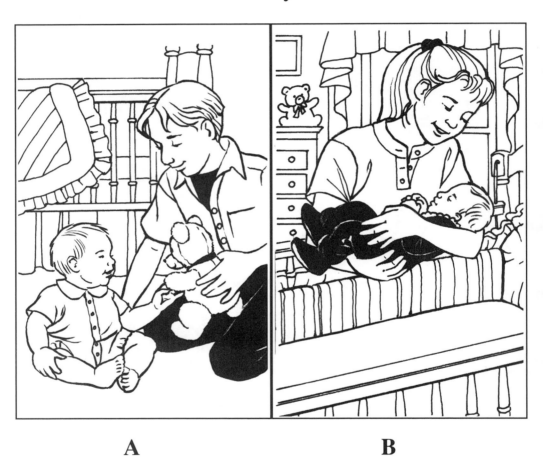

A   B

Which picture is right?

(A) or (B)

DIRECTIONS:

Help the boy down.

A   B

Which picture is right?

(A) or (B)

DIRECTIONS:

Look for it in the house.

A   B

Which picture is right?

(A) or (B)

DIRECTIONS:

Make the boat go fast.

A   B

Which picture is right?

(A) or (B)

DIRECTIONS:

Draw a picture.

A   B

Which picture is right?

(A) or (B)

DIRECTIONS:

Give the girl some flowers.

A   B

Which picture is right?

(A) or (B)

A. Exercising Your Skill

Look at the picture. Draw a picture of yourself eating the food you like best. Write a title under your picture.

B. Expanding Your Skill

Talk with a classmate about the things people do in the kitchen. Pick one thing.

Tell your classmate how to do this thing. How many steps does it take to do it?

Now it's your classmate's turn to pick one thing and tell you how to do it.

C. Exploring Language

What words do the big letters make? Follow the directions.

1. Copy the letters down the side of your paper.

I <u>ced tea</u>

2. Beside each letter, write the name of something to eat or drink.

L _____
I _____
K _____
E _____

3. Make it something that begins with that letter.

T _____
O _____

4. If you cannot think of a real food, make up a funny food!

E _____
A _____
T _____

D. Expressing Yourself

Think of a silly kind of soup, or pick one of these.

happy soup   toy soup   cake soup

Tell how to make your silly soup. Write the directions.